CAMILLE SAINT-

INTRODUCTION ET RONDO CAPRICCIOSO

for Violin and Orchestra
Op. 28

Edited by/Herausgegeben von
Maria Egelhof and Wolfgang Birtel

Ernst Eulenburg Ltd

London · Mainz · Madrid · New York · Paris · Prague · Tokyo · Toronto · Zürich

CONTENTS

Performing material based on this edition is available from Schott Music/
Der hier veröffentlichte Notentext ist auch als Aufführungsmaterial beim Verlag
Schott Music erhältlich/
Le matériel d'exécution réalise à partir de cette édition est disponible auprès de
l'éditeur Schott Music/

Full score/Dirigierpartitur/Partition directrice CON 259
Parts/Stimmen/Parties CON 259-50
Violin with Piano/Violine mit Klavier/Violon avec Piano VLB 119

PREFACE

'Nobody knows more about music all over the world than Monsieur Saint-Saëns', said Claude Debussy in praise of his fellow composer. There can be few, one might add, who have left behind such an extensive body of work, representing every musical genre: Camille Saint-Saëns (1835 – 1921) composed symphonic and dramatic music, vocal and chamber music, piano, military and ballet music – and, with *L'Assassinat du Duc de Guise* in 1908, the first original film music.

This French musician favoured the violin repertoire in particular with two sonatas, three concertos and a series of smaller works with piano or orchestral accompaniment. Some of the inspiration for these doubtless came from his friendship with the Spanish violinist Pablo de Sarasate, who delighted audiences with his circus tricks and his sweetly languishing tone on the violin. Sarasate gave Saint-Saëns many tips as to what was technically possible on the violin – and the composer dedicated his third violin concerto and the *Rondo Capriccioso* to him. It is without doubt also from his acquaintance with Sarasate that the composer acquired a fondness for Spanish tone colour and folk tunes, most clearly felt in the *Introduction et Rondo capriccioso* Opus 28, in the *Havanaise* Opus 83 and in the *Caprice andalou* Opus 122.

'With his magical bow Pablo de Sarasate took my compositions all over the world', wrote Camille Saint-Saëns in an article for the *Revue Musicale* in 1908. It was for Sarasate that he composed the *Rondo capriccioso*, which is still a highlight of the Romantic violin repertoire today. In the same article, Saint-Saëns described the piece as 'composed in the Spanish style': such exotic touches were very popular with audiences at that time. *Introduction et Rondo capriccioso* was written in 1863 and published in 1870.

An introductory recitative alternates between lyrical and playful passages. It then leads into the Rondo, where the composer gives the violin an opportunity for a furious technical firework display: this is an effective bravura piece to show off the abilities of any virtuoso violinist.

Wolfgang Birtel
English translation: Julia Rushworth

VORWORT

„Niemand kennt die Musik der ganzen Welt besser als Monsieur Saint-Saëns", lobte Claude Debussy seinen Komponistenkollegen, und nur wenige, darf man hinzufügen, haben ein derartig umfangreiches und alle Gattungen abdeckendes Gesamtwerk hinterlassen wie er: Symphonische und dramatische Musik, Vokal- und Kammermusik, Klavier-, Militär- und Ballettmusik hat Camille Saint-Saëns (1835 – 1921) komponiert, aber auch mit *L'Assassinat du Duc de Guise* 1908 die erste originale Filmmusik geliefert.

Das Geigenrepertoire hat der französische Musiker dabei besonders bedacht: mit zwei Sonaten, drei Konzerten und einer Reihe kleinerer Werke mit Klavier- oder Orchesterbegleitung. Dazu hat sicher auch die Freundschaft mit dem spanischen Geiger Pablo de Sarasate beigetragen, der das Publikum mit seinen zirzensischen Kunststücken und seinem süß-schmachtenden Ton auf der Violine verzückte. Er gab Saint-Saëns so manchen Tipp, was auf der Geige technisch möglich ist – ihm widmete er auch sein drittes Violinkonzert und das *Rondo capriccioso*. Sicherlich rührt von der Bekanntschaft mit dem Geiger auch des Komponisten Faible für spanisches Kolorit, für die Folklore des Nachbarlandes her, das am deutlichsten in *Introduction et Rondo capriccioso*, opus 28, in der *Havanaise*, opus 83 und in der *Caprice andalou*, opus 122, zu spüren ist.

„Mit seinem Zauberbogen brachte Pablo de Sarasate meine Kompositionen durch alle Länder", schrieb Camille Saint-Saëns 1908 in einem Artikel für die *Revue Musicale*. Für den Geiger komponierte er auch das *Rondo capriccioso* – damals wie heute ein Highlight im romantischen Violinrepertoire. Und als „in spanischem Stil komponiert" bezeichnete der Komponist das Werk ausdrücklich im gleichen Aufsatz: Solche Exotismen gefielen dem damaligen Publikum ausgesprochen gut. *Introduction et Rondo capriccioso* entstand im Jahre 1863 und erschien 1870.

Eine rezitativische Introduktion, die zwischen lyrischen und spielerischen Passagen wechselt, leitet zum Rondo über, in dem der Komponist der Violine Gelegenheit zu einem furiosen technischen Feuerwerk gibt – ein effektvolles Bravourstück, ein Paradestück für jeden Violinvirtuosen.

Wolfgang Birtel

PRÉFACE

« Saint-Saëns est l'homme qui sait le mieux la musique du monde entier ». C'est par ces mots que Claude Debussy faisait l'éloge de son homologue. Et, faudrait-il ajouter, bien peu de compositeurs ont laissé un œuvre aussi nombreux, couvrant tous les genres : Camille Saint-Saëns (1835 – 1921) a composé des musiques symphoniques et dramatiques, vocales et de chambre, pour piano, militaires, de ballet – mais aussi, avec *L'Assassinat du Duc de Guise* en 1908, la première musique de film originale.

Ce faisant, le musicien français a accordé une place toute particulière au répertoire du violon : avec deux sonates, trois concertos et une série de petites œuvres avec accompagnement de piano et d'orchestre. L'amitié qui le liait au violoniste espagnol Pablo de Sarasate, qui enchantait le public par ses tours de cirque et le ton langoureux de guimauve qu'il tirait de son violon, a sans nul doute contribué également à cet intérêt. Il donna maints conseils à Saint-Saëns quant aux possibilités techniques du violon – c'est à lui que celui-ci dédia son troisième concerto pour violon et son *Rondo capriccioso*. Cette relation personnelle avec le violoniste explique certainement aussi le faible du compositeur pour le coloris et le folklore espagnols, qui se manifeste le plus nettement dans l'*Introduction et Rondo capriccioso*, opus 28, la *Havanaise*, opus 83, et le *Caprice andalou*, opus 122.

« En promenant à travers le monde mes compositions sur son archet magique » c'est ainsi que Camille Saint-Saëns décrivit en 1908 Pablo de Sarasate dans un article destiné à la *Revue Musicale*. Il composa aussi pour le violoniste le *Rondo capriccioso* – à l'époque tout comme aujourd'hui un chef d'œuvre du violon romantique. Dans le même article, le compositeur indique expressément que l'œuvre est composée « dans le style espagnol », de tels exotismes plaisant particulièrement au public du temps. *Introduction et Rondo capriccioso* vit le jour en 1863 et fut publié en 1870.

Une introduction récitative alternant avec des passages lyriques et ludiques fait passer au rondo, dans lequel le compositeur donne au violon l'occasion d'un feu d'artifice technique ardent – un morceau de bravoure spectaculaire, et un morceau de choix pour tous les virtuoses du violon.

Wolfgang Birtel
Traduction: Martine Paulauskas

INTRODUCTION ET RONDO CAPRICCIOSO

Camille Saint-Saëns
1835–1921
op. 28

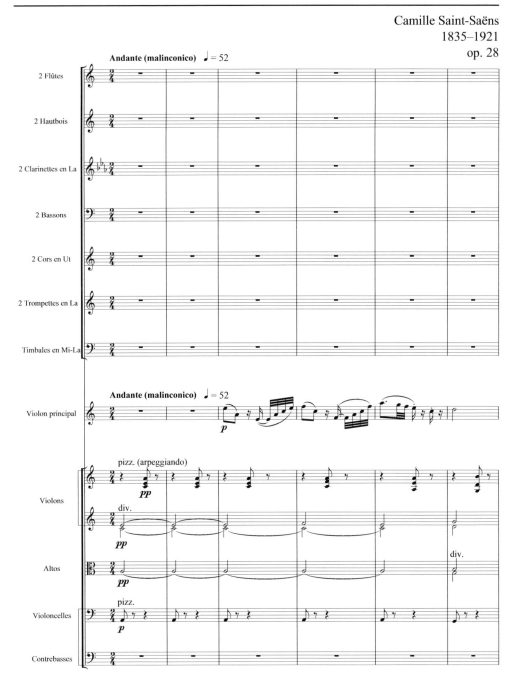

No. 1470   EE 7193

4

14

15

24

34